PUNCTUATION ★ TALES ★

commas

The Legend of Johnny Comma

by Liza Charlesworth
illustrated by John Manders

SCHOLASTIC INC.

New York • Toronto • London • Auckland • Sydney
Mexico City • New Delhi • Hong Kong • Buenos Aires

Designed by Grafica, Inc.
ISBN-13: 978-0-545-01439-7 • ISBN-10: 0-545-01439-5
Copyright © 2007 by Lefty's Editorial Services.
All rights reserved. Printed in the U.S.A.

First printing, October 2007

12 11 10 9 8 7 6 5 4 3 2 1   7 8 9 10 11 12/0

> Johnny, there are no commas in Humdinger Falls!

Comma Fact:
Commas are a very important writing tool. They separate words and ideas to help sentences make sense. This story is loaded with commas. Be on the lookout for them and try to pay attention to how they are used.

Long ago, there lived a young man named Johnny Comma. Johnny loved commas more than anything in the world. One day, a little bird told him that there were no commas in the far-away town of Humdinger Falls.

"What terrible news!" said Johnny. "I will journey west and bring the people commas."

Johnny loaded up a sack with plenty of shiny, red commas.

"Good-bye, Mom," he said.

"Good-bye, Dear," she replied. "Don't forget your hat!"

Johnny walked and walked. At last, he reached a teeny western town. There, he met a girl.

"Hi! I'm Becky Lou. Welcome to Humdinger Falls!" she said, pointing to a welcome sign.

Oh my! Humdinger Falls looked delightful, but the welcome sign was a disaster. This town DID need commas!

Comma Fact:
Commas are used to separate street, town, state, and country names, as in: *Welcome to Main Street, Humdinger Falls, Idaho, U.S.A.* Commas are also used to separate a day of the month from a year, as in: *This town was founded on June 8, 1801.*

Lickety-split, Johnny took some commas from his sack and quickly fixed the sign.

"Wow, those little critters are amazing!" said Becky Lou. "Now the welcome sign makes sense. What did you say your name was?"

"Johnny, Johnny Comma," he replied.

"Well, Johnny," she said. "Come with me. I've got a lot of folks for you to meet."

The first person Becky Lou took Johnny to meet was the owner of Bucky's General Store. The store was neat and tidy, but the signs were a mess. Bucky needed commas!

We have everything!

You can buy a pickle, broom, or wagon.

You can buy a girdle, doll, or lollipop.

Comma Fact:
Commas are used to separate three or more things in a series. One goes after each item, as in: *You can buy a pickle, broom, or wagon.*

Lickety-split, Johnny showed Bucky how to make his lists easier to understand by adding commas.

"Thanks! Those gizmos are incredible!" said Bucky. "I bet no one will make the mistake of asking me for a pickle broom or girdle doll ever again."

Next, Johnny met the owner of Tiny's Hardware Store. The store had tons of nifty tools, but the sign required one important repair. Tiny needed a comma!

Comma Fact:
The little words *and*, *but*, *or*, *nor*, *for*, *so*, and *yet* are called *conjunctions*. A conjunction along with a comma can be used to join two simple sentences, as in: *Other folks sell tools, but my tools are the best in the west.*

Lickety-split, Johnny showed Tiny how to join two simple sentences with the single word *but* and a handy-dandy comma.

"Now your slogan is much stronger," said Johnny.

"Golly," said Tiny. "How can such a cute, little curlicue have so much power?"

Hattie's Half-Moon Hotel in business since 1852 always puts a peppermint on every guest's pillow.

Then, Johnny met the owner of Hattie's Half-Moon Hotel. The hotel looked wonderful, but the sign was a wreck. You guessed it—Hattie needed some commas!

Comma Fact:
Commas can be used like parentheses to separate a detail or tangent (*in business since 1852*) from the main idea of the sentence, as in: *Hattie's Half-Moon Hotel, in business since 1852, always puts a peppermint on every guest's pillow.*

Lickety-split, Johnny added a couple of commas to Hattie's sign. And, suddenly, its meaning became clear.

"Thank you so, so, so, so much!" exclaimed Hattie. "Forget peppermints. Tonight, all my guests are getting a complimentary comma on their pillow."

Comma Fact:
Commas are often used with quotation marks to show when a speaker tag ends and dialogue begins, as in: *Becky Lou exclaimed, "LOOK!"* Commas are also used to show when dialogue ends and a speaker tag begins, as in: *"Don't worry," said Johnny.*

After that, Johnny and his new friends decided to stroll along Main Street. Johnny had a great time handing out commas to everyone he met. That is, until Becky Lou pointed to his sack and exclaimed, "LOOK!"

"There is only ONE comma left!" cried Bucky.

"Dear me!" shouted Tiny.

"How will we live without them?" shrieked Hattie.

"Don't worry," said Johnny. "I have a solution."

Comma Fact:
Commas are used to set off introductory words and phrases (*Well, So, Next, At first, As you can see, A minute later*) from the main idea of a sentence, as in: *A minute later, he buried the last comma in a patch of dirt.*

Johnny led his new friends over to Town Square. A minute later, he buried the last comma in a patch of dirt.

"There!" said Johnny, triumphantly. "Just water this spot, and pretty soon, your worries will be over."

Comma Fact:

As you can see, commas are used in many different ways. Think of a comma as a pause. If you are not sure whether or not to use one, read the sentence out loud. If you pause while reading, chances are a comma belongs in the place where you stopped.

Well, the town folks watered the spot. And Johnny was right. In no time flat, that comma grew into a giant comma tree! From that day forward, there were plenty of commas for everyone's writing needs. And good old Johnny Comma had a shady spot to read a great book.

Rule Round-Up

commas

THE BIG IDEA: Commas separate words and ideas to help sentences make sense.

This is a comma:

,

- Commas are usually used between groups of two or more adjectives.

  EXAMPLE: *He loaded up his sack with plenty of shiny, red commas.*

- Commas are used to separate the names of streets, towns or cities, states, and countries.

  EXAMPLE: *Main Street, Humdinger Falls, Idaho, U.S.A.*

- Commas are used to separate a day of the month from a year.

  EXAMPLE: *June 9, 1801.*

- Commas are used to separate three or more items, adjectives, or phrases in a series.

  EXAMPLE: *You can buy a pickle, broom, or wagon.*

- Commas are used along with little connecting words called *conjunctions* (*and, but, or, nor, for, so, yet*) to link together two simple sentences.

  EXAMPLE: *Other folks sell tools, but my tools are the best in the west.*

- Commas are used like parentheses to separate a detail or tangent from the main idea of a sentence.

  EXAMPLE: *Hattie's Half-Moon Hotel, in business since 1852, always puts a peppermint on every guest's pillow.*

- Commas are used with quotation marks to show the beginning or end of someone's dialogue.

  EXAMPLE 1/BEGINNING: *Becky Lou exclaimed, "LOOK!"*

  EXAMPLE 2/ENDING: *"Don't worry," said Johnny.*

- Commas are used to set off introductory words and phrases (*Well, So, Next, At first, As you can see, A minute later*) from the main idea of a sentence.

  EXAMPLE: *A minute later, he buried the last comma in a patch of dirt.*

TERRIFIC TIP!

Think of a comma as a pause. If you are not sure whether or not to use one, read the sentence out loud. If you pause while reading, chances are a comma belongs in the place where you stopped.

Punctuation Bingo

commas

Which of the nine sentences below use commas correctly? Mark them with buttons or pennies. Get three in a row and you win! (Bingo can be vertical, horizontal, or diagonal.)

1. Johnny Comma, who was born in 1842, always gave commas to everyone he met.

2. Becky, Lou loved to play outdoors read books draw pictures, and eat spaghetti with meatballs.

3. There is nothing better than a big bright shiny red comma!

4. I'd really, love to visit Humdinger Falls but it is so very, very very very, very far away.

5. The restaurant at Hattie's Half-Moon Hotel served tomato soup, buffalo burgers, and grits.

6. Bucky's General Store was located at 50 Main Street, Humdinger Falls, Idaho.

7. Hattie said "Commas, are even better than peppermints!"

8. Well I guess the town folks were all very happy to have Johnny come to Humdinger Falls,

9. On September 15, 1875, Tiny and Hattie got married beneath the comma tree in Town Square.

EXTRA! Write a pretend letter to Johnny Comma. In it, use lots and lots of commas—correctly!

Answers: The sentences that use commas correctly are 1, 5, 6, and 9. Bingo is 1, 5, and 9.

PUNCTUATION ★ TALES ★

commas

Meet Johnny Comma! He's heading west with a sack full of commas to visit the folks in Humdinger Falls. Why? They've never heard of this important piece of punctuation—and their writing needs help!

PQT913944

Punctuation Tales are super-funny stories designed to help children become better writers by mastering the rules of punctuation, capitalization, and sentence structure. Give kids these engaging books, and watch them laugh and learn!

Price: $3.50 U.S./$4.99 CAN.

ISBN-13: 978-0-545-01439-7
ISBN-10: 0-545-01439-5

EAN

9 780545 014397

■SCHOLASTIC

www.scholastic.com

674152

Animals That Help Us

looks at the many different ways animals help us in our daily lives. Animals...

- carry our heavy loads
- guide us when we cannot see
- protect us from danger
- are often our friends

This series looks at what makes animals good at a particular task, and how they are trained for it. Most of all, it shows how much we all rely on animals without realizing it.

Titles in the series:

ISBN 0-531-15404-1

U.S. $6.95
Can. $9.95

A FRANKLIN WATTS BOOK

Some children's homes have mini-farms where there are many different animals such as chickens, ducks, and sheep. The children enjoy holding and stroking the animals, and they also learn to look after them.

It's the children's responsibility to keep the animals clean, fed, and happy. Often, for the first time in their lives, they have someone who depends on them.

Glossary

achievement   when you have completed a task you set yourself.

breed   a type of animal within an animal family; a Labrador is a breed of dog.

commands   words that tell someone else what to do.

confidence   a sense of believing in yourself.

disobey   not doing what is instructed.

good-tempered   to have a nice nature; never being cross or grumpy.

grooming   the action of brushing or combing something; making it look neat.

handler   a person who looks after, trains, and "handles" an animal.

harness   straps around an animal's body that are attached to a leash to make the animal easy to control.

nature   the way someone or something behaves.

obedient   when a person or animal acts as instructed.

unconscious   when someone is not awake or is unaware of what is happening.

Useful Addresses

Dogs for the Deaf, Inc.
10175 Wheeler Road
Central Point
OR 97502

http://www.dogsforthedeaf.org/

Rescues and professionally trains dogs to assist deaf people and enhance their lives.

Guide Dogs for the Blind, Inc.
P.O. Box 151200
San Rafael
CA 94915-1200

http://www.guidedogs.com/

Provides guide dogs and training in their use to visually impaired people throughout the United States and Canada.

North American Riding for the Handicapped Association
P.O. Box 33150
Denver
CO 80233
1-800-369-RIDE

http://www.narha.org/

Centers across the United States and Canada dedicated to helping the disabled experience freedom, independence, and self-confidence from riding.

Index

ANIMALS THAT HELP US

Animals Helping with Special Needs

Clare Oliver

W

FRANKLIN WATTS

A Division of Grolier Publishing

NEW YORK • LONDON • HONG KONG • SYDNEY
DANBURY, CONNECTICUT

Picture Credits:

Cover: Frank Spooner (Godlewski/Liaison)

Interior Pictures: John Birdsall pp. 5b, 10, 11b, 28b; Canine Parnters for Independence pp. 17t, 17b, 18b, 19t, 19b; Bruce Coleman pp. 4 (Jane Burton), 25t (Hans Reinhard); Sally and Richard Greenhill Photo Library p. 21b (Sally Greenhill); The Guide Dogs for the Blind Association pp. 5t, 6, 7t, 8t, 8b, 9t, 9b; Robert Harding p. 26 (I. Van der Harst); Hearing Dogs for Deaf People pp. 13t (both pictures), 13b, 14t, 14b, 15t, 15b; Image Bank p. 11t; Natural History Photographic Agency p.23b (A.N.T.); Only Horses pp. 20, 21t; Rex Features pp. 7b (Richard Sobol), 16 (C. Brown), 24 (Sunstar); Riding for the Disabled Association pp. 22 (Basil Birchall), 23t (Gartmore R.D.A. Group); RSPCA pp. 12; South West News Service p. 25b; Frank Spooner p. 18t (L. Marescot); The Stock Market p. 29 (Ariel Skelley); Support Dogs p. 27b; Tracey Morgan Animal Photography pp. 24t, 28t.

Series editor: Helen Lanz
Series designer: Louise Snowdon
Picture research: Sue Mennell
Special Needs consultant: Dr. Philip Sawney

First published in 1999 by Franklin Watts

First American edition © Franklin Watts 1999
A Division of Grolier Publishing
90 Sherman Turnpike
Danbury, CT 06816

Visit Franklin Watts/Children's Press on the Internet at:
http://publishing.grolier.com

A catalog record for this title is available from the Library of Congress.

ISBN: 0-531-14564-6 (lib. bdg.)   0-531-15404-1 (pbk.)

Copyright © Franklin Watts 1999

Printed in Malaysia

Contents

Extra Care

Have you ever wondered why there is often a fish tank in the dentist's waiting room? Watching fish swim around helps people relax and stops them from thinking about having their teeth drilled.

Other pets can help us feel better, too. Having to look after an animal — whether it is a small tortoise or large pony — is a big responsibility. It helps make us feel wanted. We take care of ourselves, so we are fit to look after our pets.

Some people need extra care because they have special needs — and animals can help them as well.

People who can't see, for example, may use dogs to guide them. Dogs have also been trained to help people who find it hard to hear.

For people who are physically challenged (who have difficulty moving), working with animals improves their co-ordination and builds their confidence.

Riding is good exercise and improves balance.

Eyes That See

The very first guide dogs for blind people were trained in Germany after the First World War (1914–1918). Soldiers who had been blinded during the war were given guide dogs to help them in their daily lives.

An American woman named Mrs. Harrison Eustis realized that all blind people — not just soldiers — would find a dog a useful companion.

Mrs. Eustis set up "*L'Oeil Qui Voit*" ("the eye that sees") in Switzerland — the very first organization that trained guide dogs for blind people.

Mrs. Eustis traveled all over the world to give talks about her work.

Animal Anecdote

Morris Frank became the first guide dog owner in the United States. With the help of Mrs. Eustis, he learned how to work with Buddy, his guide dog.

Buddy was trained in Switzerland and then went to the United States to be with Morris Frank.

Dogs are excellent at this sort of work. They enjoy being with people, they learn quickly, and they are usually obedient and do as they are told.

Today, there are programs for training guide dogs worldwide. This man and his guide dog live in South Korea.

Puppy Programs

Puppies start guide dog training when they are 6 weeks old.

Not all the puppies put forward for the training program will be chosen. Each puppy is tested to see whether it is gentle and whether it is clever enough for the job.

Labradors and Golden Retrievers are the most popular guide dog breeds.

The puppy lives with a "puppy walking" family for the first year. Family members make sure the puppy learns to recognize as many sights and sounds as possible. They take it to busy shopping centers, train stations, restaurants — and obedience classes.

Families with young children make excellent puppy walkers.

If the puppy shows it can learn quickly, it goes back to the training center. Here, it is shown how to travel on buses and trains. It is taught to walk around things that a person would not be able to walk under, such as railings. By the end of its training, the dog will understand about 20 commands.

The dog is taught to disobey a command that would lead its handler into danger.

The dog spends the final four weeks of its training with its owner-to-be, getting used to his or her voice. The owner is also trained in how to handle the dog. It is usually the beginning of a long, rewarding friendship.

Each dog learns to obey spoken commands and tugs of its harness.

9

Horse Sense

Horse riding might seem a difficult hobby for someone who cannot see, but it is an excellent way for blind people, as well as sighted people, to relax and build up their confidence.

Grooming, as well as riding, the horses helps people learn how to handle the animals.

Horses that are ridden by blind people are chosen for their quiet, gentle natures. Horses that are easily scared are no good for this kind of work.

Often, the horses have already had one career working with people. Many horses in riding schools for blind people are police horses who are too old for police work. These horses have already had a lot of training and are always well behaved.

Police horses are used to heavy traffic and won't jump or rear up at sudden noises.

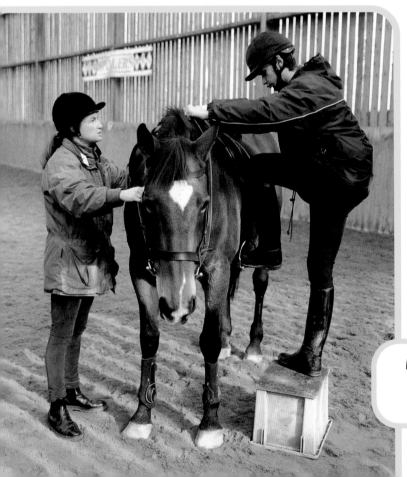

The horses have more training at the riding school. They must learn to be very careful with their riders. Blind riders cannot see a low-hanging branch that could knock them out of the saddle. The horses are trained to walk around any dangers like this.

Instructors encourage the riders to do as much as they can for themselves.

Hearing Dogs

For people who have difficulty hearing, a trained dog companion can make a big difference. "Hearing dogs" have been used for over 20 years. Today there are training programs for hearing dogs all over the world.

Like a guide dog, a hearing dog has a close friendship with its owner.

The dog's first task each day is to nudge its owner awake when it hears the alarm clock go off. All through the day the dog alerts its owner whenever there is a noise that the owner needs to respond to.

The dog touches its owner with its paw if the oven timer goes off or the baby cries. It leads its owner to someone who is calling from another room or to the door if the bell rings.

Both dog and owner are trained together.

Animal Anecdote

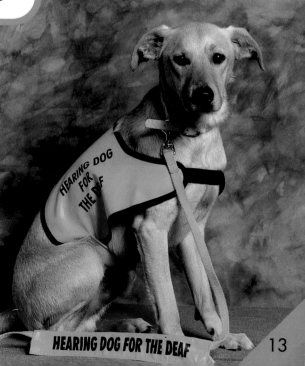

Usually hearing dogs lead their owners to a sound — but not when it's a smoke alarm. Shirley-Ann's hearing dog, Max, knew just what to do when he heard the smoke alarm go off next door. He touched Shirley-Ann on her leg and then lay down — the sign for danger. Thanks to Max, the fire department was called and the fire was put out.

Max was given an award for his quick thinking.

HEARING DOG FOR THE DEAF

Training Hearing Dogs

Most hearing dogs are mongrels. The breed of dog does not matter, as long as the animal is bright and good-tempered.

Like guide dogs, hearing dogs start their training by living with a family.

Families who take hearing dogs are called socializing families. This dog was the 1,000th puppy to be placed with a family in Britain.

HEARING DOG PUPPY

Many of the dogs are from rescue centers. They have often been left by their first owner. With time and patience, they can become good hearing dogs.

Serious training starts once the dog has been taught basic obedience skills.

Each dog is taught different commands, depending on the special needs of its new owner.

The dogs learn by being praised when they do the right thing.

The dog learns the sound of its own doorbell and leads the trainer to the door when it rings. Each dog is also taught not to do anything if it hears a different type of doorbell.

After training, the dogs are given a yellow coat to wear to show that they are fully trained hearing dogs for a deaf person.

When out and about, hearing dogs wear their yellow jackets.

Assistance Pets

People who are physically challenged find some everyday tasks very frustrating. Living with an assistance pet can make a real difference. The animal is trained to help with certain tasks — and is a friend to its owner as well.

Monkey helpers have proved so useful that their owners are able to work from their own homes.

Capuchin monkeys make good assistance pets. Because monkeys have hands like ours, they are able to do things that would be impossible for any other animal. They are clever enough to use machines — such as CD, tape, and video players.

Dogs make very good assistance animals, too. Golden Retrievers and Labradors are chosen for their friendly, calm natures. They like to fetch and carry things, which are important tasks for any assistance animal to do.

The dogs are trained to pick things up, get things out of bags, and carry the shopping bags.

Assistance dogs are more than everyday helpers. They make their owners feel safe, and they give them a new sense of freedom. And, above all, they are good companions.

On the Job

Monkeys that are chosen to be assistance pets spend the first five years living as part of a volunteer family. Then the tame monkeys spend a year at a training center. There they learn to recognize commands to do many different tasks.

Most monkey helpers are bred at centers where they are specially trained for the job.

Dogs also go through different stages of training. Suitable puppies are chosen and placed with a volunteer puppy walking family for a year. The dogs then continue their training for another six months at a training center. There they learn over 90 spoken commands.

Dogs can help when things are difficult to reach.

It's important that each trained animal is matched carefully with its new owner. The owner and assistance dog go on a two-week training course. Someone will then visit them in their home to make sure the partnership is working.

The owner and dog stay together only if they get on well with each other.

Animal Anecdote

After Allen's car accident, he was introduced to Endal, an assistance dog. Endal helps Allen dress by fetching his clothes for him. He also helps Allen around the house.

"Having Endal helped me to accept that I had a disability," says Allen. "But best of all, being responsible for Endal has stopped me thinking about myself all the time."

The Power to Move

Riding a horse can help people with physical disabilities and can also be great fun. Riders can enjoy the thrill of being on horseback. At the same time, they can concentrate on exercising certain muscles or parts of the body.

Someone always walks by the side of the horse. This helps the riders feel safe. They know that someone is there to catch them if they fall.

The riding teachers choose exercises that suit each person's needs. Someone who does not have good balance might learn to move from facing forward to facing backward on the horse as it walks on slowly. Or the person might be asked to lean forward and pat the horse.

In time, riders build up the confidence to go over jumps and enter competitions.

Animal Anecdote

Dan has cerebral palsy, a condition where his brain has difficulty controlling the movement of his body's muscles.

Dan says, "I love it when I am on a horse. When I sit in the saddle and the horse starts to move, I feel free!"

Making Friends

Some people have learning difficulties.
They might not be able to concentrate
on one thing for very long, or be able to
follow instructions.

Riding in groups is fun.
You meet lots of new people.

People with learning difficulties sometimes
find it hard to be with other people.
They may not like to talk or may find it
upsetting if there is any change in their routine.

Horse riding can be a good way to encourage people with these special needs to mix with others. Riders discover that a simple kissing noise can urge the horse to move again after it has stopped. They learn that by making a sound, they have the power to make things happen.

Children often become friends with their horses and soon learn to form friendships with other people, too.

Animal Anecdote

Heather was only three years old when she started riding. To begin with, she didn't want to get onto Allison the horse, but once she was in the saddle, she was soon enjoying herself.

Before she started riding, Heather hardly talked at all. She learned that she could control what Allison did by giving commands. After two years of riding, Heather is a chatterbox — but her very favorite words are "Allison" and "horse."

23

Swimming with Dolphins

At the Human Dolphin Therapy Center in Miami, children with learning difficulties swim with dolphins — and the dolphins seem to work magic.

Children usually spend two weeks at the center. Therapists work with the children to improve their speech and massage their bodies. And the children swim with the dolphins every day. Just being with the dolphins relaxes the children.

Some experts think that it makes the children feel special that such beautiful, wild creatures want to spend time swimming with them. Perhaps it's not surprising that sharing the dolphins' games has a magical effect on people.

Dolphins enjoy playing with other dolphins, too. They are wonderful to watch in the wild.

Animal Anecdote

Nikki was born in 1990 with brain damage. Until 1998 he had never spoken a single word. Then he went swimming with dolphins in the Miami Center.

Amazingly, after just a few swims, Nikki spoke his first word. He said "in" — because he wanted to get back in the water to be with the dolphins.

Special Powers

People with epilepsy live full lives like everyone else. Epilepsy is a condition where the brain produces too many messages at once. When this happens, the person can become unconscious and fall — this is called a seizure.

Someone with epilepsy may have a seizure without any warning. It can be very dangerous if the person falls in an awkward place.

Often we do things that could be very dangerous if we had a seizure.

A seizure-alert dog can sense that a person is going to have a seizure about half an hour before it happens. The dog is trained to warn its owner that a seizure is coming.

When the dog senses that a seizure is going to happen, it may stare, bark, or paw at its owner as a warning.

Owners and dogs have a strong friendship.

The person then knows to find a place where he or she will not be hurt if a seizure starts.

Having a seizure-alert dog allows people with epilepsy to do things they otherwise would not have the confidence to do.

Pets as Therapy

People who live on their own often feel lonely. This can happen to anyone at any age — whether they are old or young. Feeling that no one cares is hard — and then a pet's endless love can make a big difference.

A pet provides good company in return for being well looked after.

PAT (Pets As Therapy) animals are ordinary pets who live with ordinary families. But once or twice a week they go and visit people in nursing homes or hospitals. Dogs, cats, and even rabbits are used — the main thing is that the animal is gentle and friendly toward strangers and enjoys being petted.

This bunny visitor has certainly brought a smile to its friend's face!